Dave Ward

i
impact books

Jess

First published in Great Britain in 1993 by
Impact Books Ltd, 151 Dulwich Road, London SE24 0NG

ISBN 1 874687 32 3

Acknowledgements are due to the following, where these pieces were first published or broadcast:
Alternative Sounds, Anarchism Lancastrium, BBC School Radio, Both Sides Of The River, Cat Ate
The Dog's Dinner, Cheapo Review, City Fun, Dial-A-Poem (Merseyside), Die Horen (Germany), Diversion,
Graffiti, Greenwich Sound Radio, Gutted, Hat, Here We Go, I Wish I Had The View, In Touch (Hodder &
Stoughton), The Incurable, The Indy, Kicks, Krax, Killin Time, Liverpool Weekly Review, Ludd's Mill,
Mon Cheri (Holland), Morrocci Klung!, Moth, Next 14, Oxford Road Show (BBC 2),
Perfectly Acceptable, Radio Hallam, Ramraid Extraordinaire, Sandwiches, Slow Dancer, Smart Verbal,
Smoke, Sol, Something To Leave Behind, Speakeasy, Sphinx, Start, Stride Cassettes,
Summer Salt, Ten Commandments, Toxic Grafity, Transatlantic Review, Ugly Duckling.

A selection was also published as a pamphlet by Windows in conjunction with
Paul Weller's Riot Stories Ltd.

Special thanks to Aware Photographic Workshop.

Printed in Great Britain by Redwood Books, Trowbridge, Wiltshire

"JAMBO ACE"
"JAMBO COOL"

Jambo sees his name now wherever he goes -
on empty walls and bus shelters where
he sprayed it months ago.

You don't need a famous name to be famous anymore.
Just get yourself a spray can and the whole town
knows who you are.

Jambo lives in a street called "No Ball Games". It must be —
there's no other street signs left on the estate. The council
never bother about putting the names back up. All the fire-
engines and taxis and ambulances get lost every time they come
here.

The council can't afford to build playgrounds. And they can't
afford to replace street names. But they can always manage to
come round and put up brand new signs saying "No Ball Games".
Then the kids just rip them down again. It's the only game
left to play.

Jambo doesn't like watching telly. But the telly likes watching him. It would watch him all day if he'd let it. Right through the kids' stuff in the morning, right through the racing in the afternoon, right through the news, and the film, and the news, and the film, and the snooker. Right till it's time to turn off. The telly likes to watch Jambo.

Just to see what he does all day. Picking his nose, picking his feet, picking out winners, falling asleep. Getting up to make a cup of tea, then letting it go cold beside him on the floor. Scratching himself and reading the paper. Wondering whether to go out. Wondering if his mates are coming round. Looking at the time. Picking his nose. Falling asleep.

The telly likes to watch Jambo. Right till it's time to turn off. Just to make sure he wakes up in time to go to bed.

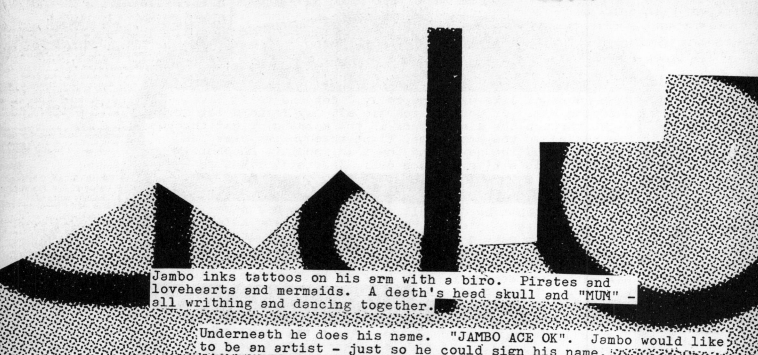

Jambo inks tattoos on his arm with a biro. Pirates and lovehearts and mermaids. A death's head skull and "MUM" - all writhing and dancing together.

Underneath he does his name. "JAMBO ACE OK". Jambo would like to be an artist - just so he could sign his name.

But he can't be bothered with paintings. Paintings take too long. So he just signs his name in all the places where they ought to be. On empty walls, on the back of bus shelters, on the sides of houses, on the stairs in tower blocks... JAMBO ACE OK.

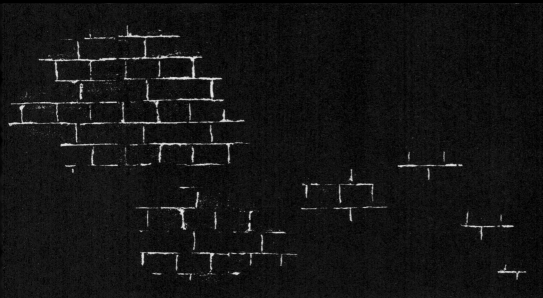

Jambo's been sitting in exactly the same position for an hour now without moving. Staring at one spot on the floor, emptying his mind of everything he can remember. Jambo is trying Transcendental Meditation.

In the background, voices chanting. A roomful of people all meditating, staring at their own private spot on the floor, trying to sort out their problems, or gazing up at bright coloured posters on the wall.

Jambo is trying Transcendental Meditation. That's not what he calls it, but that's what he's doing. And whatever you call it, you might as well do it because there's nothing else to do while you're sitting till your turn comes up in the waiting room at the social security.

Jambo kicks a ball hard against the wall. As if
he's trying to burst it, or make the wall fall down.

No-one kicks Jambo. No-one gets him down.
He tells himself every time he kicks the ball
and the wall just kicks it back.

Sun sets slowly, sliding down the bricks, until it's not
a ball he's kicking - only shadow. Kicking the shadow
of a ball until he can't see anything at all.

But still Jambo keeps on kicking back.

Jambo breaks the bottle. Like a whole city of sirens. Howling winos. Like an army of football fans stamping down the street smashing windows and chanting as they come. A heavy metal orchestra snarling out of control.

Jambo grips the jagged neck as if he's wrestling with demons. Flings it like a hand-grenade high over the wall.

Jambo's cold.
Cold night to be standing out under the lampost
hanging round waiting for his mates to come and wait there with
him.

There always seems to be someone missing.
They always just need someone else - for a game of football,
to pay for a round, to go down town... But whoever it is,
he never shows up, so they never do anything,
just carry on waiting.

Jambo's cold. No-one's come at all. Kicks at the wall,
wondering where they are. Wonders if they've all gone off
somewhere else and they're just standing there
waiting for him.

Jambo sniffs glue and petrol fumes.

It gives him a buzz but then it makes him feel sick and he
wonders why he does it but he can't seem to stop.

He does it every day, every time he steps outside for a
breath of fresh air and the wind's coming in off the
motorway, past the paint works and the chemical base and
the glue factory...

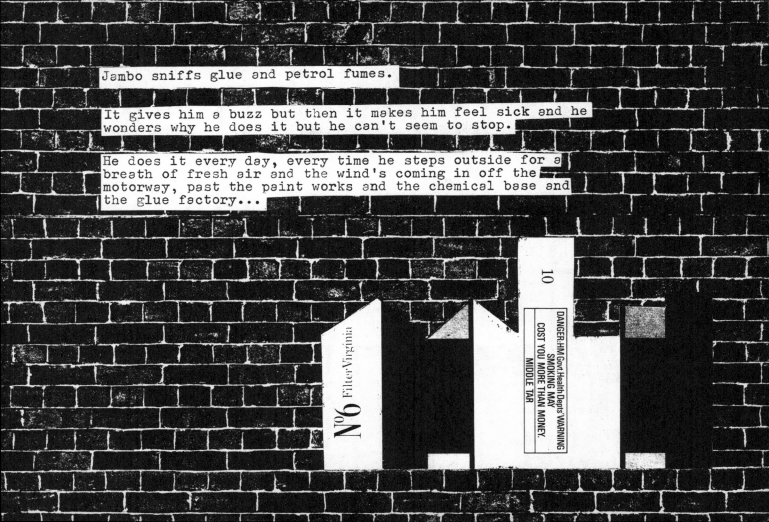

Jambo playing football on the back field. His jeans rolled up to his knees covered in mud. Boots with no studs slipping and skidding. No-one watches except the tall cooling towers of the power station in the distance. No-one cheers him on.

But as soon as Jambo scores, he's floating across the turf of Wembley Stadium. The stray dog yapping at his heels that jumps up to lick his face is the team captain's bristly embrace. And the women on the landings in the block of flats behind are the crowds on the terraces, waving banners that aren't really wet sheets after all. Even the hard-faced kids skiving off school round the back of the burnt-out garages look like they might want to line up for his autograph.

Jambo punches the air as he climbs the railings to drag the ball out of a clump of nettles. He doesn't care. A goal is a goal, and when you score you're a winner not a loser - it doesn't matter where you are.

...er punch for ...ers.
...en Devonshire and ... Pike got in a ...ble tangle, leaving ...atmore with time to ...in a shot from eight ...ds.

...Devonshire made up for ...is slip by controlling the second half and when Dusan Nikolic tackled the England midfielder on the edge of the box, the ball broke to Trevor Brooking, who calmly slotted in the equaliser.

...it Blackpool! It ...oks like Fourth Division soccer for the first time at Bloomfield Road next season.

And the agony of this once famous club was sad to see as they struggled for a win that might have given them a faint chance of survival.

A wholehearted gutsy performance was needed and it was totally lacking.

Not that Carlisle looked anything but an ordinary side: they just had the vital edge in match winner Peter Beardsley, who stamped his class on the game from the start.

And Beardsley slid past two men to put a fiercely angled shot past Ian Hesford for the winner.

SALFORD VAN HIRE

I DON'T BELIEVE IT! Everton's Paul Lodge looks on in ...
'keeper Gary Bailey gets down to ...

OS BEATEN
TO

WREXH...

WREXH...
point
Ran...

Jambo waiting for the football paper. Waiting to see if they won. Waiting to see who scored.

Waiting to read the minute-by-minute report like a script for everything everyone'll be saying nonstop in the pub tonight.

And the next day going through it all again. Muddled memories jerking through goals like out-of-focus action replays.

(0)..0 Leeus...
(0)..0 Man. U...
25.854: Rowell
Sunderland...
25.450: ...
(1)..4 st Brom...
Brighton (0)..
...0.22 Gregory
...st Brom. C. (1)..
... Robson
...shom (0)..0

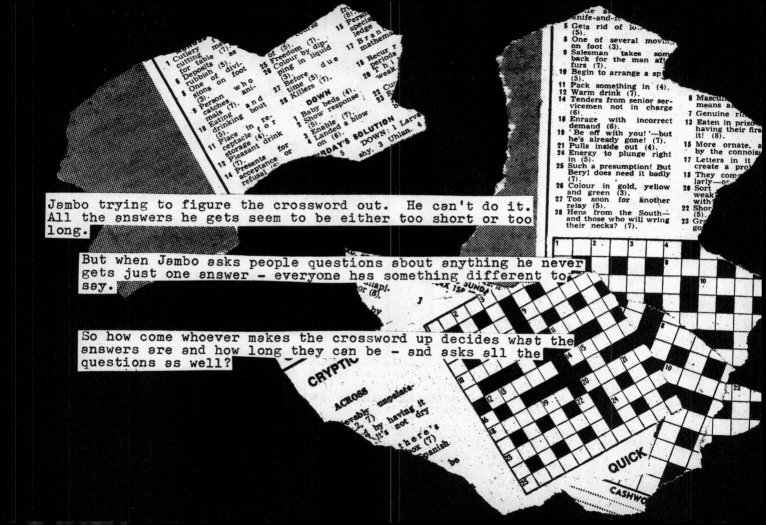

Jambo trying to figure the crossword out. He can't do it. All the answers he gets seem to be either too short or too long.

But when Jambo asks people questions about anything he never gets just one answer - everyone has something different to say.

So how come whoever makes the crossword up decides what the answers are and how long they can be - and asks all the questions as well?

Jambo likes loud music. Likes to play his records loud
with the windows open wide so all the street can hear.

No-one else in the street seems to like his music -
but Jambo doesn't care. Just sits on the window sill
and stares straight back when they stare up at him.

Instead of staring up at him and trying to make out they don't
like music when he sits on his window sill and plays
his records loud enough for all the street to hear.

Jambo thinks everyone should play loud music. And get out
into the street and dance. In and out of each other's houses,
dancing different dances for every different sound.
Playing loud music all night long and not bothering to get up
for work in the morning.

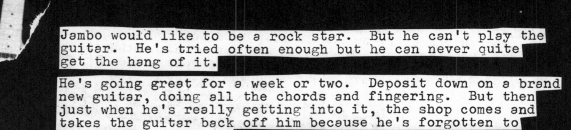

Jambo would like to be a rock star. But he can't play the
guitar. He's tried often enough but he can never quite
get the hang of it.

He's going great for a week or two. Deposit down on a brand
new guitar, doing all the chords and fingering. But then
just when he's really getting into it, the shop comes and
takes the guitar back off him because he's forgotten to
keep up the payments.

Jambo wants to be the world's first rock'n'roll star to go on
tour when he's dead.

He hasn't quite sorted the stage act out, but he knows it'll
be a sensation. Everyone'll be there to see it.

And the live album of the tour's bound to sell millions as well.
Rock'n'roll stars always make more money when they're dead.

Jambo goes in the record shop. He asks the girl behind the counter if they've got the new single by The Blank.

The girl looks at him like he's just used bad language and tells him they only stock singles in the chart.

Jambo looks around the shop then and asks if they've got the new one by The Zips. The girl drums her fingers on the cash till and slowly shakes her head.

Jambo looks puzzled and reminds her it's riding high in the charts.

The girl behind the counter shrugs. It's in the Top Three. It's sold out.

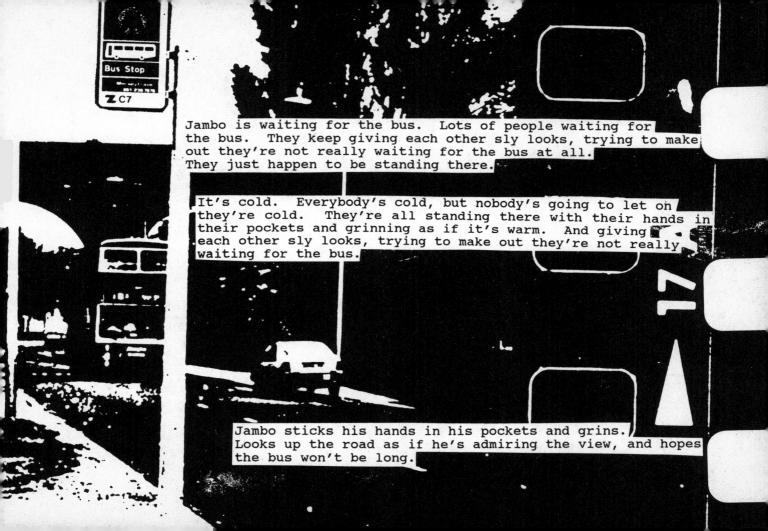

Jambo is waiting for the bus. Lots of people waiting for
the bus. They keep giving each other sly looks, trying to make
out they're not really waiting for the bus at all.
They just happen to be standing there.

It's cold. Everybody's cold, but nobody's going to let on
they're cold. They're all standing there with their hands in
their pockets and grinning as if it's warm. And giving
each other sly looks, trying to make out they're not really
waiting for the bus.

Jambo sticks his hands in his pockets and grins.
Looks up the road as if he's admiring the view, and hopes
the bus won't be long.

Jambo picks daffodils. He can't think of a reason why, except
he's climbed into someone's garden and there's nothing else to
do now he's here. So he picks all the daffodils because the
bright sunshine makes him, but when he gets outside in the street
again he can't think what he'd say to anyone who asked him why
he's got them - so he gives them away to an old lady in a wheel-
chair and goes off whistling, hoping it wasn't her garden.

Jambo keeps having these bad dreams where he gets sent back
to school. Sat at a desk taking the exams all over again.
Staring out the window and scratching his head with a pen.

They told him if he failed he'd never get a job. But Jambo's
not bothered - he's got what he wants already.

At school no-one paid him, but he still had to work and get
ordered around like a kid. Now he's on the dole and gets
paid for doing nothing, and does whatever he wants.

He's just worried about these dreams. The mornings he wakes up
and it's nine o'clock and he goes to dive down the stairs. And
then he remembers he's got nowhere to go and he might just
as well stay in bed.

Jambo trained for his profession before he left school.

He used to practise every day. Signing his name on desks and walls. The careers teacher told him he was so good at it he ought to be a signwriter.

So now Jambo does it full time. And he still gets plenty of practice. They test him to make sure he hasn't lost his touch every time he signs his name down the dole.

MITCHELL BROS
SCRAP
MERCHANTS

CASH
BUYERS
& ROPE

PROMPT
COLLECTION

BEST PRICES
STEEL.
CAST IRON

OPEN
8-5.30 MON-FRI
SAT. 12.00

NON FERROUS
METALS
BRASS · LEAD
COPPER · ETC

FACTORY
CLEARANCE
DISMANTLING

-WANTED!
- USED
BATTERIE

Jambo sitting on the wall. It's a great day for sitting on the wall. Watching all the people going to work and staring at Jambo, wishing they didn't have to go to work, wishing they could spend all day sitting on the wall, just like him.

So there can't be anything wrong with sitting on the wall - not if that's what everyone else would do if they could. But the looks that Jambo gets when he's sitting on the wall, you'd just think it was a crime.

If anything bends, Jambo will bend it.

If anything breaks, Jambo will break it.

If anything is set solid in concrete, Jambo will have to lean on it, just to see if it moves.

He knows that if he doesn't, Jambo will end up being the one who gets leaned on, bent and broken.

ROAD CLOSED

Jambo looks over his shoulder. He keeps thinking someone's following him. Jambo looks over his shoulder, but he can't see anyone there.

Then he wonders if they're waiting for him, round a corner, on the stairs.

He's not even sure who they are anymore. He just knows there's someone there.

He turns the next corner suddenly. Just another street. Stands and listens for the sound of feet. Silence.

Jambo looks over his shoulder.

It's raining. Jambo stands in the shop doorway and
watches the girl who's singing to him. He sees her
face over and over again on dozens of different TV
screens. Black and white, colour, sharp and clear
or out-of-focus. The same girl singing over and
over again like a choir, her mouth opening and
closing in time with herself. And Jambo can't
hear a sound.

Jambo looks out at the rain. People pushing along the
street, eyes gazing down at their feet, no-one saying
anything. Everywhere seems to silence. Everyone deaf
and dumb in the rain.

Jambo meets this man who gets Jambo to buy coffee while he sits and tells his life story.

Jambo doesn't really like coffee - not the way they make it in this cafe anyway. But it seems to be such a long life story that coffee helps to pass the time.

Jambo's gazing out the window while he listens. He wonders if the man would like to hear his life story, but he's not sure if he'll get a chance. The man's hardly started on his own.

Jambo decides they need more coffee. To save time, the man keeps talking while Jambo's up at the counter. Jambo's not sure if that's right...he might miss some of the exciting bits (he's sure there must be some exciting bits somewhere, or the man wouldn't bother telling him) - and after all, Jambo is paying.

Jambo carries the coffee back to the table. The man carries on with his story. Jambo carries on looking out the window while the man spoons spoon after spoon of sugar into his coffee. Then drinks it quick.

Jambo watches an old lady crossing the road wearing a red and purple overcoat and odd gloves, and wonders if she's anywhere in this story. She'd brighten it up. Turns round and finds the man's finished his own coffee and started on Jambo's now.

Jambo doesn't reckon that's right. Not if he's paying and he doesn't even get a chance to tell his own life story. So he tells the man he's got a bus to catch, gets up and walks out.

But the man doesn't stop...he carries on telling his life story, to pass the time while he sits and waits for someone else to come along and buy him coffee.

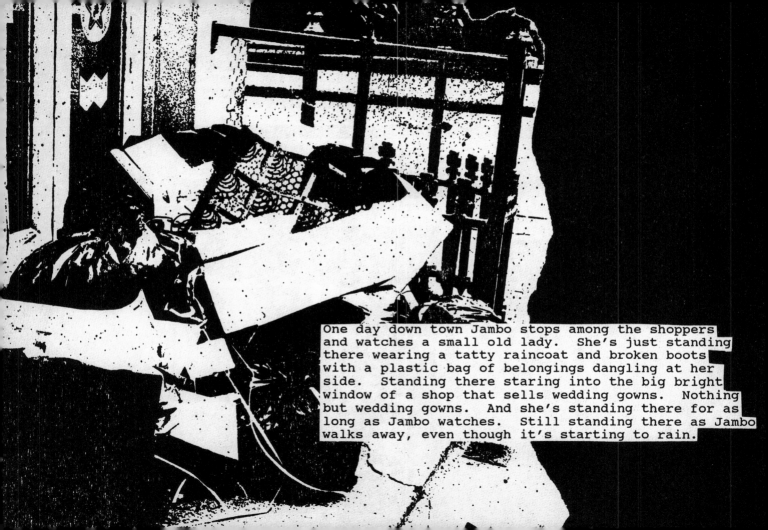

One day down town Jambo stops among the shoppers
and watches a small old lady. She's just standing
there wearing a tatty raincoat and broken boots
with a plastic bag of belongings dangling at her
side. Standing there staring into the big bright
window of a shop that sells wedding gowns. Nothing
but wedding gowns. And she's standing there for as
long as Jambo watches. Still standing there as Jambo
walks away, even though it's starting to rain.

Jambo picks his nose, waiting for the chippie to open. Leaning
on the wall by the door. He's given up peering through
the window. Watches the dogs across the road instead, ripping
through the litter bins, rooting in the rubbish, pulling it
out and into the gutter.

A cop car comes past. Slows down and stares at him. Jambo
glares back. They'd make a law against waiting outside
the chippie if they could.

Doddering Thomas, wandering to the off-licence to see if it's
open. Empty bottle stuck under his arm ready for a refill
to take back to his flat to sit and drink in front of the telly
that won't work anymore, though he likes to pretend. He even
changes channels twice a night because he never could stand
watching the news.

The off-licence is shut, so he's got to wait, just like Jambo.
Though he always tries to make it look as if he's not waiting
at all. He just happens to be out for a walk. Jambo watches
him cross the road, still clutching his bottle. Checking the
bins where the dogs have been to see what they've left behind.

Jambo picks his nose. Kicks his heel against the chippie door.
Nowhere's open and it's starting to rain. Even the cop car's
got nothing to do but crawl back round again.

Jambo lies in bed. Listening to the wind blowing up and down
the street. He can't get to sleep. The wind rattling and
clattering at dustbin lids like a drunk coming home.

Lying in bed, Jambo dreams a huge man, knocking on the window,
trying to knock him awake.

Shouting at Jambo with all the voices of everyone in the street,
his mouth slamming open and shut like a door with a broken lock.
Muttering and grumbling like someone waiting for their dole.
Wailing like a baby, roaring like the old man who's going blind
but still has an eye for all the young wives.

All the street is in his room. Bawling and shouting and falling
everywhere. Drinking and smoking and swapping jokes. Jambo
tries to tell them it's time to go home, but they just stare
right through him as if they've always been here, as if they're
going to stay here, right here in Jambo's room.

Jambo won't get out of bed.
No-one can get you out of bed
if you don't want to.

Someone is trying to get Jambo out of bed.
Someone is hammering at the door.
Sunshine hammering at his eyeballs.
It's today again.

Jambo never likes today.
He goes back under the bedclothes,
looking to see what happened to yesterday,
dreaming about tomorrow.

Someone is hammering at the door.
Someone is trying to get Jambo
out of bed.

No-one can get you out of bed
if you don't want to.

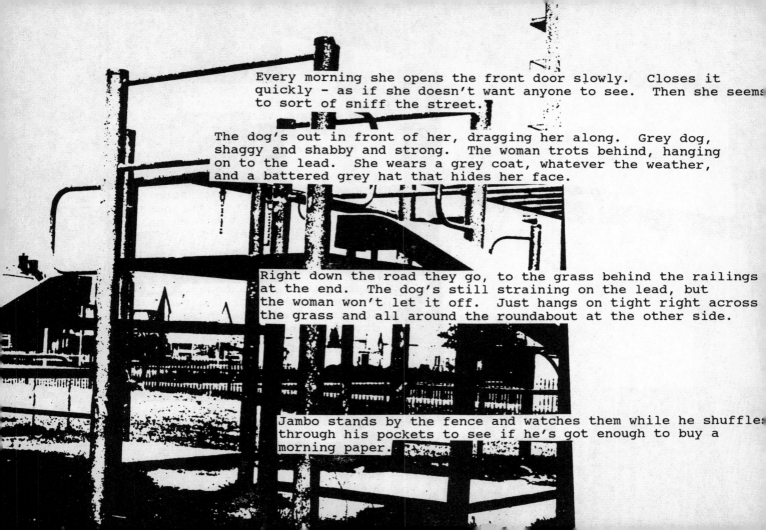

Every morning she opens the front door slowly. Closes it
quickly - as if she doesn't want anyone to see. Then she seems
to sort of sniff the street.

The dog's out in front of her, dragging her along. Grey dog,
shaggy and shabby and strong. The woman trots behind, hanging
on to the lead. She wears a grey coat, whatever the weather,
and a battered grey hat that hides her face.

Right down the road they go, to the grass behind the railings
at the end. The dog's still straining on the lead, but
the woman won't let it off. Just hangs on tight right across
the grass and all around the roundabout at the other side.

Jambo stands by the fence and watches them while he shuffles
through his pockets to see if he's got enough to buy a
morning paper.

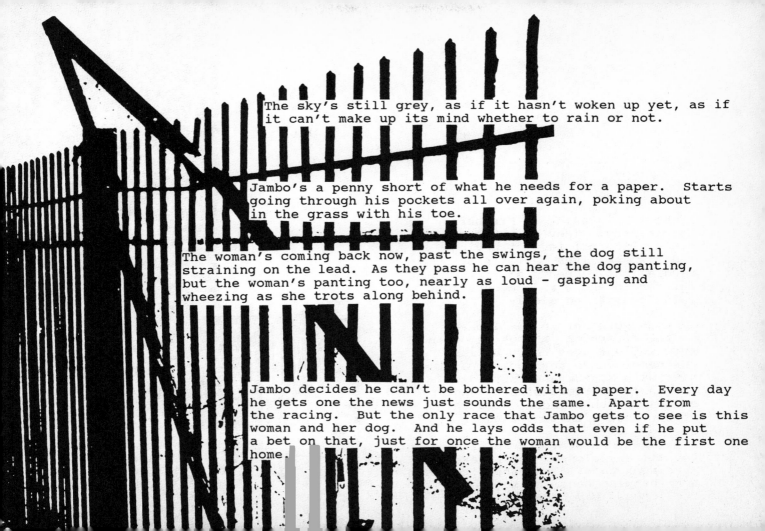

The sky's still grey, as if it hasn't woken up yet, as if it can't make up its mind whether to rain or not.

Jambo's a penny short of what he needs for a paper. Starts going through his pockets all over again, poking about in the grass with his toe.

The woman's coming back now, past the swings, the dog still straining on the lead. As they pass he can hear the dog panting, but the woman's panting too, nearly as loud - gasping and wheezing as she trots along behind.

Jambo decides he can't be bothered with a paper. Every day he gets one the news just sounds the same. Apart from the racing. But the only race that Jambo gets to see is this woman and her dog. And he lays odds that even if he put a bet on that, just for once the woman would be the first one home.

Jambo is listening to Mrs Doris
complaining. They've cut her
electricity off for not paying
and now she lives her life by
candlelight. Spends all the time
she can in shops and laundrettes.
Doing everything slowly.

He even sees her in the library
in the afternoon, though he doesn't
know why she goes there because
she never reads any books. Just
sits with a newspaper spread on
the table in front of her, and
stares out the window, scratching
at her head with bony fingers.

Sometimes she stays there till
the library closes - never even
turning a page. Then she picks up
her shopping bags and sets out
the longest way home.

Right the way past the playground
where she watches the kids on the
swings. Right past the corner shop
and Mrs. O'Casey's. Then when she
reaches her own street she seems to
linger by every window seeing if
she can see inside. Peering at
everyone else's telly till she gets
to her own door and lets herself in.
Groping to the back kitchen
she strikes a match and lights the
gas ring. Cooks her supper to eat
by herself by the light from one
unromantic candle.

Then she goes and sits by the window.
Watching the people as they pass
outside. Staring at every face
lit up in the glow from the street-
lamp. Trying to smile and wave
at them, but always failing. Sitting
in the window, by her candle,
complaining.

Freeze frame. Jambo slopes like
a ghost across wasteland. Tall
buildings haunt him, flickering
into vision in the memory
of his eye. But every time he
stops to look they've gone.

Everything's gone. The terraces
of houses, corner shops and pubs,
snug rooms packed with smoky
laughter.

This was home for Jambo's
favourite auntie and all his
uncles, Nan and Grandad, his
cousins and their mates.
But now everyone's flitted like
shadows out to the new estates.
Banged up in tower blocks serving
time for crimes no-one's invented
yet.

And when they do escape they drift
back here, where the moss grows
thick in the cracks between crooked
pavingstones, and thistledown
blows blurred across the gaps where
the houses were.

They wander lost tracks through
alleys and doorways that no-one can
see anymore, pretending the only
reason they come is to check for
rich pickings in the city centre
supermarkets, even though all the
special offers on the dizzy rows
of shelves won't even save the cost
of the bus fare they have to pay
to get here.

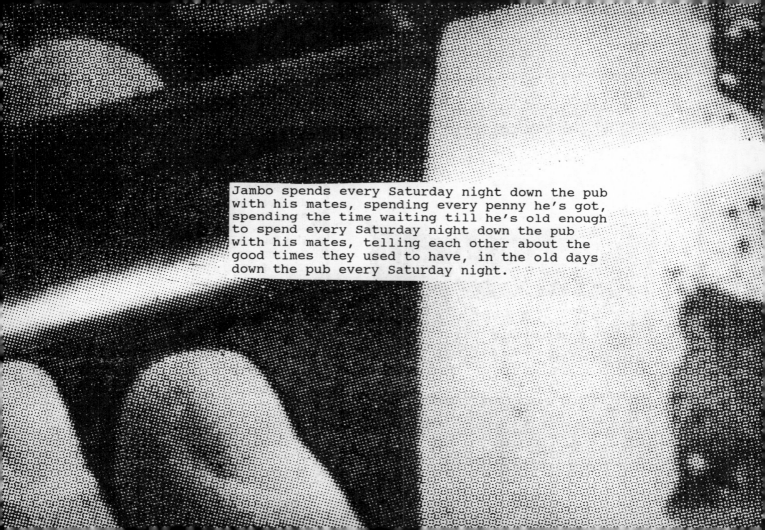

Jambo spends every Saturday night down the pub
with his mates, spending every penny he's got,
spending the time waiting till he's old enough
to spend every Saturday night down the pub
with his mates, telling each other about the
good times they used to have, in the old days
down the pub every Saturday night.

Jambo sat in the pub, listening to people drinking. Drunken words.

Nothing anyone says makes any sense to Jambo, but he's not sure if that's because he's drunk or they're not sure if that's because he's drunk or they are.

He's not even sure if they make sense to each other any more.

Jambo always buys the War Cry in the pub so his mates can do the crossword. It's the only way he knows to keep them quiet so that he can put what he wants on the jukebox.

Jambo reckons he must have bought enough War Cries to pay for his place in heaven. And he'll be up there with all the greats - Elvis and Buddy Holly and Eddie Cochran. And his mates'll still be down below, trying to do the War Cry crossword.

The kid next door to Jambo keeps singing
Elvis Presley songs every night,
with the record player turned up full.
His bedroom window is plastered with posters of
Elvis Presley.
On the front door he's got a big sign that says —
"ELVIS IS THE KING".

Jambo went round and ripped it off,
and stuck up another one that said
"THE KING IS DEAD, JAMBO RULES".

It's not that Jambo doesn't like Elvis Presley.
He just can't stand the kid next door.

Jambo slips a coin in the jukebox and sticks a record on. This week's Number One. Everyone sitting at their tables dancing to it without knowing that's what they're doing.

Tapping spoons against their teacups, fingers drumming across the tabletop. Shuffling feet to the rhythm.

Suddenly the record jams. Grinding out the same line over and over again. Everybody stuck like a still from a film — fingers, feet and teaspoons all hanging in midair. Nobody even speaks...

Jambo goes over and gives the jukebox a kick. The needle skids across and the record starts again. Everyone comes back to life — tapping their teaspoons, drumming their fingers, shuffling feet, just as if nothing had happened.

Now Jambo's the jukebox discjockey. He just stands there grinning, dreaming up what he's going to get everyone to do next time the record jams.

Jambo gets in the empty flat through a gap where one of the nailed-up planks round the back is missing.

Someone used to live here. Just empty rooms now. Rags in the corner, dog shit on the floor. All the meters, pipes and wiring ripped out. Paper torn off the walls. Thin light squeezing through the holes between the boards where the windows were.

Someone used to live here. Someone used to sit in this room and watch the TV, there by the socket in the corner. Someone used to sit here and drink cups of tea and listen to the neighbours going up and down the landing outside.

Jambo wanders out into the hallway. Sifts through the leaflets stuffed through the letterbox advertising everything 2p off at the supermarket two weeks before. But no letters for anyone anymore.

Climbs the staircase slowly, boots clattering on the bare boards. He pauses on the landing - all the doors are closed. He hears a sound from one of the rooms, turns to go, then hears it again and it's only the wind.

He pushes the door open. A small room. And posters still stuck on the wall. Last year's pop stars, fading now and torn. Pile of magazines strewn all over the floor. Must have been a girl's room. Jambo wonders how old she was. She must have sat here, on the bed, listening to her record player, sticking up pin-ups, staring at herself in her mirror as she put on her make-up ready to go out.

Ready to go down town. Jambo wonders who it was. Might even have been that girl at the disco he always wanted to get off with. And now Jambo's right here in her room, just like he always wanted – and she doesn't even know.

AND I'LL ALWAYS BE THANKFUL...THAT THESE EYES OF MINE CAN'T SEE YOU

THE END

Jambo fell in love with the girl
on the circus trapeze the first
time he saw her when he was a kid
He'd have followed her round the
world and back if he could.
He didn't know then that she was
old enough to be his mother.
But now he can see every line
on her face even when she's
right up high under the lights.

Now when she's in town it's her who
follows Jambo round. But Jambo doesn't
want to know. He's just watching
the way the Muscle Man is watching
the way the Trapeze Girl is watching him.
Jambo's trying to guess if the Muscle
Man's still as strong as he was the time
he bent the park gates apart to get Jambo'
head out when Jambo was climbing back
through one night.

He didn't know then that Jambo was
trying to run away with the Trapeze Girl.
Now he isn't, but the Muscle Man
thinks he is. And Jambo wishes he'd
listened to the old Escape Artist who
offered to teach him a trick or two,
one winter afternoon.

Jambo's an escape artist. It's the only thing he's ever learnt.
Always getting out of everything he can.

Getting out of changing his socks till they smell so bad
his mates have a whip round to buy him a new pair.

Getting out of footie training. He just keeps fit by running
away every time he has to do twenty press-ups.

Getting out of getting up. If he stays in bed till bed time
it saves getting undressed again.

Doing nothing at all for as long as possible except when
he's making up excuses for not doing anything, then complaining
there's too much to do.

Telling lies to explain the lies he told the day before about
what he was really doing the day before that.

Jambo's an escape artist. Always on the run. It's the only way
he's ever seen it. He doesn't think it's wrong. He knows what
he wants to get out of - and he knows the way it's done. The
only trouble is, every time he gets away, he can never think
where it is he wants to go.

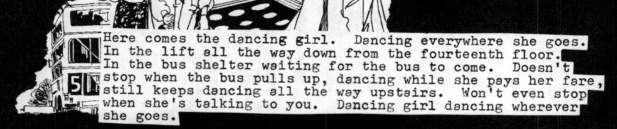

Here comes the dancing girl. Dancing everywhere she goes.
In the lift all the way down from the fourteenth floor.
In the bus shelter waiting for the bus to come. Doesn't
stop when the bus pulls up, dancing while she pays her fare,
still keeps dancing all the way upstairs. Won't even stop
when she's talking to you. Dancing girl dancing wherever
she goes.

So Jambo just wonders why the only time she stops and sits
down is when he gets up and asks her to dance at the disco.

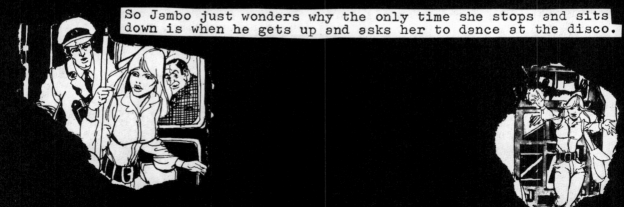

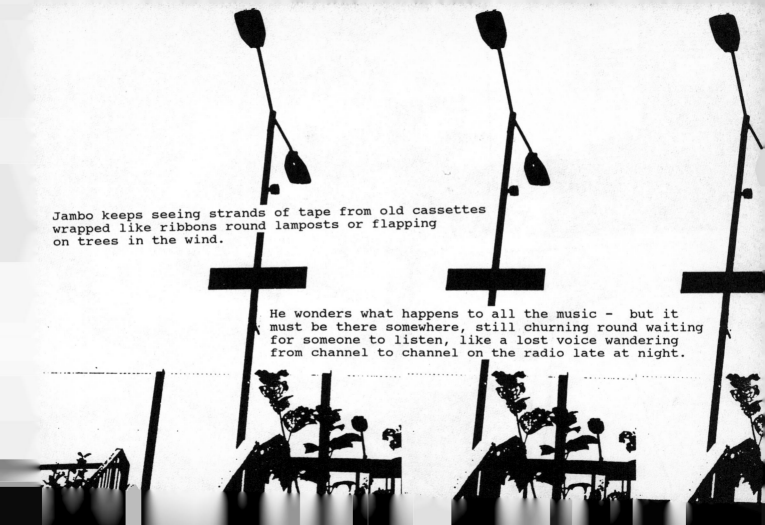

Jambo keeps seeing strands of tape from old cassettes wrapped like ribbons round lamposts or flapping on trees in the wind.

He wonders what happens to all the music - but it must be there somewhere, still churning round waiting for someone to listen, like a lost voice wandering from channel to channel on the radio late at night.

It's Friday the Thirteenth. Jambo
uncrosses his fingers and ducks
under the ladder. No bricks or
slippery paint-pots fall on his head.

Jambo never gets much luck any other
day of the year, but he reckons
bad luck's good luck the other way
around - and Friday the Thirteenth
makes him feel like his birthday's here.
And just to show he's right,
there before his eyes, is a warm damp
fiver, lying on the ground.

Jambo grins and sweeps it up, straight
into his back pocket. Stops and checks
to make sure it's not the one with the
hole in it.

Someone's lost a fiver, but Jambo's
five pounds better off. And he bets
whoever dropped it copped the paint-pot
as well.

Jambo's always wanted to see himself on television. He never thought he'd get the chance, but here he is sitting watching himself.

His mates all grin and giggle when he comes on the screen. It's not a good shot - you can't see him properly, then he turns round and the camera's right on his face.

The next bit's all muddled. It's not really in focus. You can't see what's happening or what Jambo's really doing with his back to the camera.

This is the bit where the store detective says he's putting things in his pocket. And Jambo keeps on telling her he was only pretending, just so he could see what he looked like on the playback - because he's always wanted to see himself on television.

Jambo likes buying badges. He stands there for ages outside the shop, staring at them in the window, reading all the jokes and slogans over and over again.

But then when he finally decides which one to buy, and pins it on the front of his jacket, he can't read what it says anymore. He can't even see it, so he forgets he's got it on. Then he starts to wonder why everyone keeps pointing at him and grinning and laughing as he walks down the street.

Jambo in limbo. Hanging like
a dancer half-way under the bar.
He's stuck. Doesn't know if
he's drunk or sober.
Halfway to the floor or getting
back on his feet.

It's the heat. And something
wrong with his boots. He keeps
falling over. Time to go. But
Jambo can't remember where it was
he was going. Another drink.
He's a little bit dizzy so
another drink will get him fit.

He feels sick. Out here in the
backyard. Gazing up at the stars.
Gazing down at his feet. Far,
far away. There's something wrong
with these boots.
They can't walk straight.

Jambo thinks they need another
drink.

Jambo feels like someone out of
those old silent movies. He's
got the funny walk alright, but
he reckons that's because the film
keeps slipping. Every few seconds
there's another frame missing.

As he zig-zags down the street
in hazy grey and white he can hear
the crazy pianist dancing on the
keyboard. Then there's a flash
like a bomb with no sound.
Jambo's thrown upside down.

The projectionist's making out
with the usherette
and left the film spewing all
across the floor.

Jambo lies in the gutter listening,
but he can't hear anyone laughing
anymore.

There's a knock at the door. Jambo opens it. It isn't one of his mates, but it's too late to close it now. Jambo stands hypnotised by the wild staring eyes of a man in a suit with a briefcase full of glossy brochures. The man starts to ask Jambo if he's prepared for the final destruction of the entire world. Jambo can't work out if he's a Jehovah's Witness or if he's just selling insurance.

Jambo writes a suicide note every night. He writes it slowly. For himself. For nobody else to read. He lists the reasons why.

At the bottom he writes how he's going to do it. And then he goes to bed.

In the morning he wakes up. And reads the note. First thing. Before he does anything else.

Every morning, after breakfast he burns the note. He never keeps them. But every day they are different. The way he plans to do it is different.

It makes him feel good. To wake up again every morning, and know he's still alive. It's like being born again.

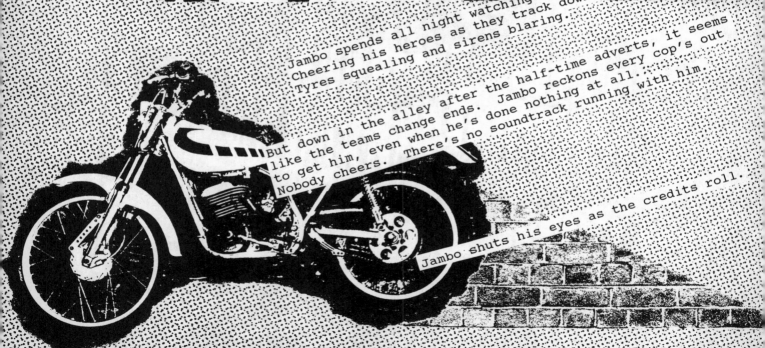

Jambo spends all night watching cop films on the telly. Cheering his heroes as they track down the villains. Tyres squealing and sirens blaring.

But down in the alley after the half-time adverts, it seems like the teams change ends. Jambo reckons every cop's out to get him, even when he's done nothing at all. There's no soundtrack running with him. Nobody cheers.

Jambo shuts his eyes as the credits roll.

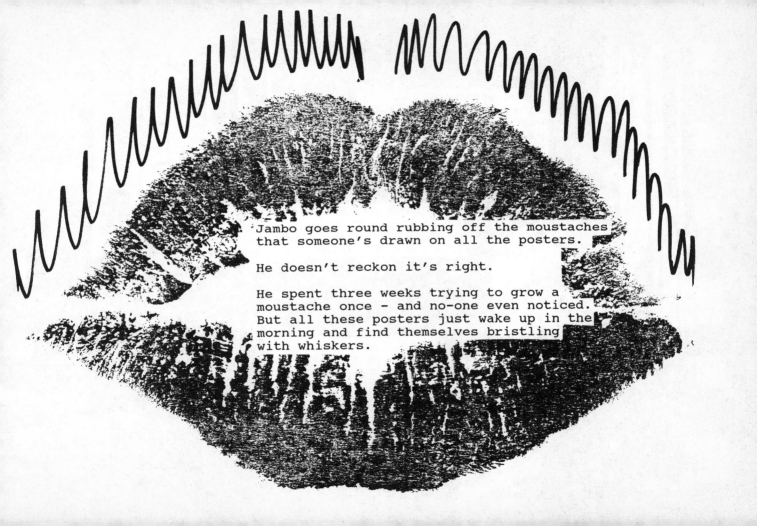

Jambo goes round rubbing off the moustaches
that someone's drawn on all the posters.

He doesn't reckon it's right.

He spent three weeks trying to grow a
moustache once - and no-one even noticed.
But all these posters just wake up in the
morning and find themselves bristling
with whiskers.

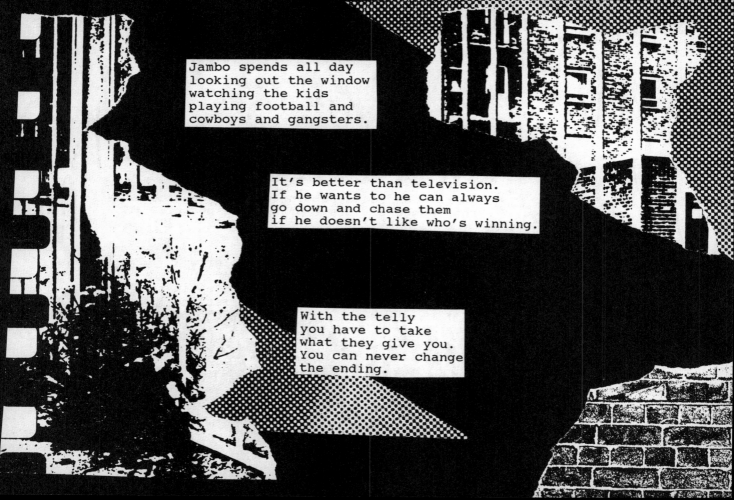

Jambo spends all day
looking out the window
watching the kids
playing football and
cowboys and gangsters.

It's better than television.
If he wants to he can always
go down and chase them
if he doesn't like who's winning.

With the telly
you have to take
what they give you.
You can never change
the ending.

Get it right

Thre jet isnt engh spce on it

Jambo lies in the bath. His head right down under the suds. The water up over his ears.

You can't hear anything when you're in the bath with the door shut tight. Can't hear kids screaming and the road drills outside. Can't hear the cars winding out of the factory. Can't hear the people next door through the wall. Can't hear the voices that threaten and jibe.

All Jambo can hear is the silence in his head, filling the bubbles till it grows so big he could climb inside and lie there, just listening.

"Stop biting your nails," says Jambo.

"I can't help it. It stops me worrying,"
Mandy tells him.

"I've got plenty to worry about,"
Jambo retorts.
"But I don't go round biting my nails."

"No," Mandy mutters. "You just smoke."

"Well, so do you."
Jambo takes her hand.
"You've got nicotine on your fingers
and chewed up nails."

"I know," Mandy sighs.
"I'm worried about giving up smoking."

"Do you know if you dream in colour
you're supposed to be creative?....
I dream in colour.
What do you dream in?" Mandy asks.

"Black and white," says Jambo.

"Oh. What do you dream about?"
Mandy asks.

"Werewolves, Dracula. Tom and Jerry."
Jambo tells her.

"They're all off the telly," Mandy says.

"I know," Jambo replies. "I've only got
a black and white telly."

"I keep having these dreams about
that actor off the telly,"
says Mandy.
"The one in the sports car advert."

Jambo snorts, "So what?"

"I dream I'm having it off with him,"
Mandy explains.

"So what?" repeats Jambo, picking his nails.

"Doesn't that make you jealous?"
Mandy wants to know.

"No," Jambo tells her.
"I have dreams as well you know."

"What sort of dreams?" Mandy's curious.

"I keep having these dreams where I _am_
the actor in the sports car advert."
Jambo blows his nose.

"I keep having these dreams
where I can fly,"
says Jambo.

Mandy tells him dreams about flying
are really dreams about sex.

"Oh," says Jambo.
"What does it mean if you keep having
dreams about sex?"

Jambo and Mandy unwind from each other.

"Ugh," growls Jambo. "Your lipstick
tastes foul."

"Ugh," slurps Mandy. "Your toothpaste
tastes vile."

They look long and hard at each other.

"I'm not wearing lipstick," says Mandy.

Jambo shakes his head.
"I ran out of toothpaste three days ago."

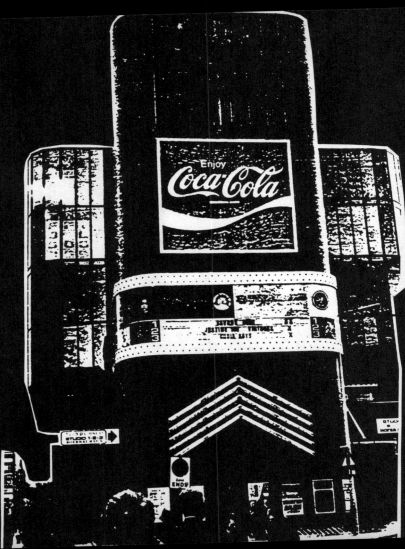

Jambo's face in the mirror. Looks like a record cover.

Jambo fancies himself as a record cover. Only trouble is, record covers never smile. Never dance, never drink. Never do anything.

They just stay stacked away on the shelf, staring at each other, like faces in mirrors.

Jambo pulls on his jacket. It's a new jacket. It feels like a fighting jacket.

Jambo looks at himself in the mirror. He feels like he could fight anyone in a jacket like this.

He just hopes he won't have to. He doesn't want to ruin his new jacket.

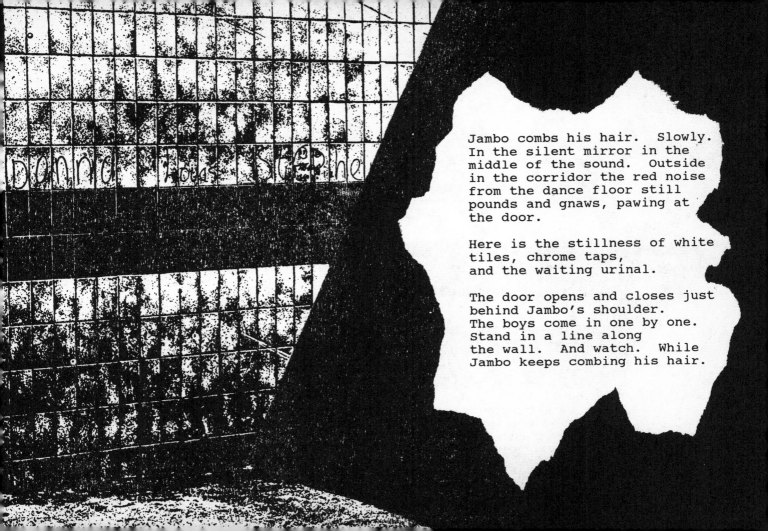

Jambo combs his hair.   Slowly.
In the silent mirror in the
middle of the sound.   Outside
in the corridor the red noise
from the dance floor still
pounds and gnaws, pawing at
the door.

Here is the stillness of white
tiles, chrome taps,
and the waiting urinal.

The door opens and closes just
behind Jambo's shoulder.
The boys come in one by one.
Stand in a line along
the wall. And watch. While
Jambo keeps combing his hair.

At the party no-one dances. Heavy heads lolling off shoulders.
The record player lies sick in the corner. The girl in
the garden is singing.

Jambo props up the wall. He keeps repeating the telephone
number of someone he wants to talk to. Stumbles through
the bathroom door. Takes the lipstick off the girl in the
mirror. She wants to kiss him but he just gets her face
and writes the number across it in crazy red figures.

All around the house, Jambo writes up the number. All over
the wallpaper. Another pattern that doesn't make sense.

The girl who's having the party is up in her mother's bedroom
with her best friend's boyfriend. Her best friend is wandering
around the house reading telephone numbers and talking
to everyone about a film she once saw.

She can't remember its name. But in the film there was a party.
In black and white. In an old house. And a girl in a dress
just like her's who danced with everyone. Until she was
spinning round and round and the telephone rang and she answered
it and ran screaming from the house and across the lawn towards
the waiting trees...

Jambo can't remember the number. Every time he starts to write
it up he has to go back to the last one and read it and try to
remember and then copy it out again.

No-one else can read it in the end. No-one would even know
it was a number. Just a red blur.

Jambo goes out into the garden. The girl sits in the uncut
grass. She sings a song with no words. Jambo just wants
to listen. He doesn't want to talk to anyone anymore.

In the house the telephone rings. No-one can hear it. Upstairs
in the bathroom a girl with a red telephone number scrawled
across her face is being sick on the floor.

Drift. Through deserted squares and unlit streets.
A city asleep. Coming home from a party that never
even started.

Spent half the night in front of the mirror deciding
what to wear. Hair rinsed in the kitchen sink and
still not dry.

Out down the pub and no-one there except Jambo again
and getting drunk too quick and going to the party
and not knowing anyone and not wanting to know anyone
and nobody dancing and throwing up and falling down
and in the distance the fight.

These streets stagger with no home to go to. Through
the railings and across the grey park. Under the trees.
The party's over. It never even started.

SAMBO CHEWS GUM

EVERYONE'S CHEWING GUM

BLOWING BIG...

PINK BUBBLES

LIKE WHEN SOMEONE'S TALKING IN CARTOONS....

EXCEPT THEY'VE GOT NO WORDS IN THEM!!

LATER....

JAMBO WONDERS IF THAT MEANS ...

NO-ONE'S GOT ANY-THING TO SAY

BUT YOU CAN'T SAY ANYTHING ANY-WAY WHEN YOUR MOUTH'S FILLED UP WITH...

GUM!!

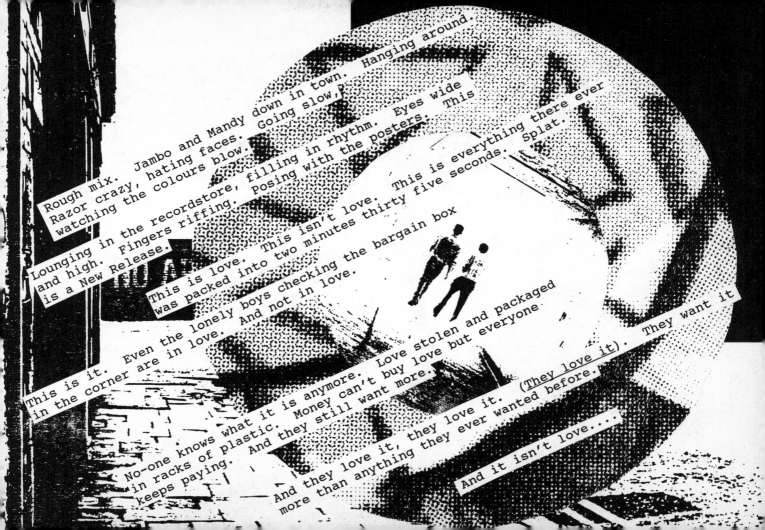

Rough mix. Jambo and Mandy down in town. Hanging around.
Razor crazy, hating faces. Going slow,
watching the colours blow. Eyes wide

Lounging in the recordstore, filling in rhythm. Eyes wide
and high. Fingers riffing. Posing with the posters. This
is a New Release.

This is love. This isn't love. This is everything there ever
was packed into two minutes thirty five seconds. Splat.
Even the lonely boys checking the bargain box

This is it. Even the lonely boys checking the bargain box
in the corner are in love. And not in love.

No-one knows what it is anymore. Love stolen and packaged
in racks of plastic. Money can't buy love but everyone
keeps paying. And they still want more.

—— And they love it, they love it. (They love it). They want it
more than anything they ever wanted before.

And it isn't love....

DAILY EXPRESS

DAILY EXPRESS

ECHO
its so nice to come home to

Daily Mirr

ECHO
its so nice to come

Daily Ma

CENTRAL
FARM

OPEN 78

4 - D

Dusk. The bus queue shuffles. Silent as the staring faces
plastered across the hoardings. Bright mouths smiling
that never speak.

Dumb eyes watch the buses come and go.
Jambo watches the woman on the corner who sells the evening paper
watching the advertisements watch the shop-window models
watching the bus queues. No-one ever speaks to her. Just giv
her the money and walk away with columns of long silence
to fill the bus ride home.

At the end of the telephone line. A voice
is hanging.
This is where it starts. This is
how it ends.
It is always like this. There is
no start. There is no end.

High wire nerves. Knives in the kitchen.
Dull glaring eyes strip the street. Panic
of small change and too many children
and not enough wine.
Not enough time.

The voice was young once. This is
where it starts.
It was always like this.

A daze of streetlamps and dancing. In the front parlours the televisions are dead. In cold back kitchens lovers twist positions between tables heavy with hunger.

Dark rum and bluebeat. Dub reggae rhythm. Open doorways. Children thrust between drunken legs.

Sad as jazz, lost saxaphones unravelling endless backstreets.
Bad blues of alleyways, empty bottles, as kids sit on the steps
of the cellar club. The slow dust blows from hand to hand.
Street lives spread all over the wall where no-one will ever
read them.

Blunt silence. Then the girls whisper, hurried shadows huddled
under tall walls, hanging over railings. No money, no money....
a jukebox tune jammed in their heads. Low voices steal broken
moments. Plundering lovers, opening dreams. Cool eyes looting.

These dull bricks ache with echoes. Against the night.

Mandy wakes every morning with metal dreams. Heavy moons in her head. Aching rhythm. Unfinished visions decay inside her like dull shadowy paintings.

Room full of trash comics and throw-away clothes she never gets a chance to throw away. Lipstick she never wears for men who never come.

Curtains undone like another bad dream. Birdsong choked in petrol fumes. Brick wall sky and factory smoke.

Turns the radio on and the deejay's the only man who gets in here. He talks too much. All the time about nothing at all. The sort of man she wouldn't want in her street, wouldn't let in the house and would never ever have in her room.

But he's the only one. Who gets here every time.

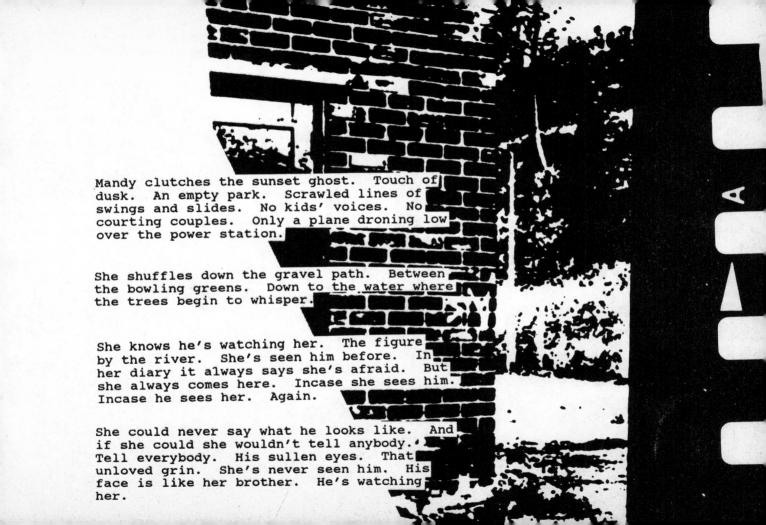

Mandy clutches the sunset ghost. Touch of
dusk. An empty park. Scrawled lines of
swings and slides. No kids' voices. No
courting couples. Only a plane droning low
over the power station.

She shuffles down the gravel path. Between
the bowling greens. Down to the water where
the trees begin to whisper.

She knows he's watching her. The figure
by the river. She's seen him before. In
her diary it always says she's afraid. But
she always comes here. Incase she sees him.
Incase he sees her. Again.

She could never say what he looks like. And
if she could she wouldn't tell anybody.
Tell everybody. His sullen eyes. That
unloved grin. She's never seen him. His
face is like her brother. He's watching
her.

"What's up with you?" Mandy asks.

"I've got a hangover," Jambo complains.

"What do you mean?" Mandy looks puzzled.
"You never even went out last night."

"I know. But I <u>always</u> get a hangover
on Sunday mornings."

Jambo holds his head in his hands.

"I'm just keeping in practice."

"You're wearing my football shirt,"
says Jambo.

"I know," Mandy tells him.
"I want to wear it down the disco."

"But I need it," says Jambo.

"What for?" asks Mandy.
"I thought you'd been dropped from the team."

"I have," Jambo tells her.
"I want to wear it down the disco."

"How come you never dance
down the disco?" asks Mandy.

"I keep falling over," Jambo explains.

"What's the point of going to the disco
if you're not going to dance?" asks Mandy.

"There's a bar there," Jambo tells her.

"I know," says Mandy. "All you ever do
is drink so much you end up falling over."

Jambo and Mandy pull the wishbone.

"What did you wish for?" Mandy asks him.

"I'm not telling you," Jambo says.
"If you tell anyone what you wished for
you never get it."

"I know what you wished for,"
Mandy strips a chicken bone.
"And I know you're not getting it anyway -
so it doesn't make any difference."

"I bought you a box of chocolates," Jambo whispers.

"What for?" Mandy wants to know.

"Well, that's what you're supposed to do, isn't it?"
Jambo asks.
"In all those old movies you keep watching, the hero's
always buying chocolates."

"Thanks," Mandy mutters.
"But I can't eat them. I'm on a diet."

She pushes the box into Jambo's lap.
"I bet you knew that, didn't you? I bet you're not
being romantic at all. I bet you got them to eat yourself.
Well - go on then, I don't care..."

Jambo slowly rustles through the wrappers.
" - I don't like chocolates," he says.

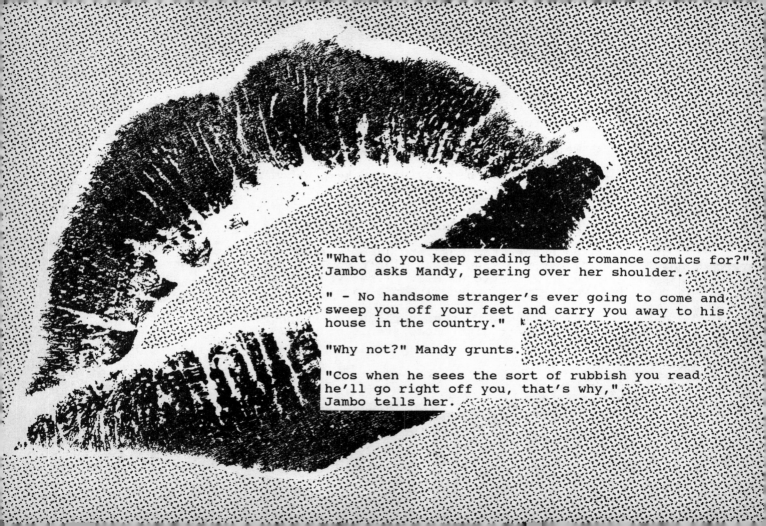

"What do you keep reading those romance comics for?"
Jambo asks Mandy, peering over her shoulder.

" - No handsome stranger's ever going to come and
sweep you off your feet and carry you away to his
house in the country."

"Why not?" Mandy grunts.

"Cos when he sees the sort of rubbish you read
he'll go right off you, that's why,"
Jambo tells her.

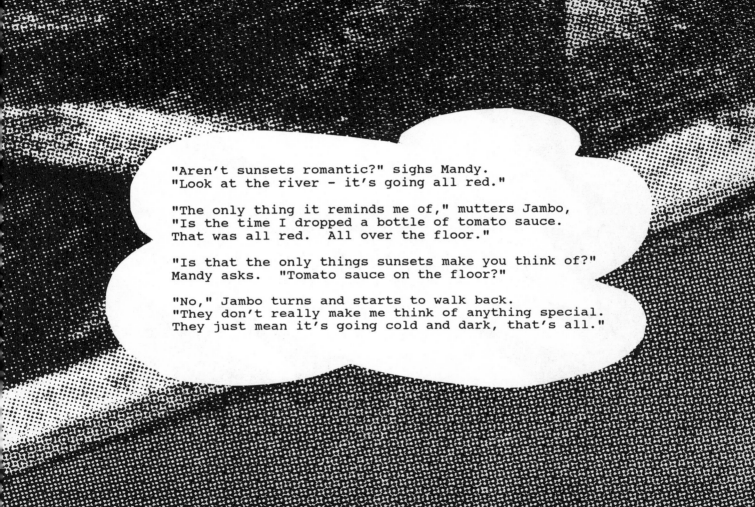

"Aren't sunsets romantic?" sighs Mandy.
"Look at the river - it's going all red."

"The only thing it reminds me of," mutters Jambo,
"Is the time I dropped a bottle of tomato sauce.
That was all red. All over the floor."

"Is that the only things sunsets make you think of?"
Mandy asks. "Tomato sauce on the floor?"

"No," Jambo turns and starts to walk back.
"They don't really make me think of anything special.
They just mean it's going cold and dark, that's all."

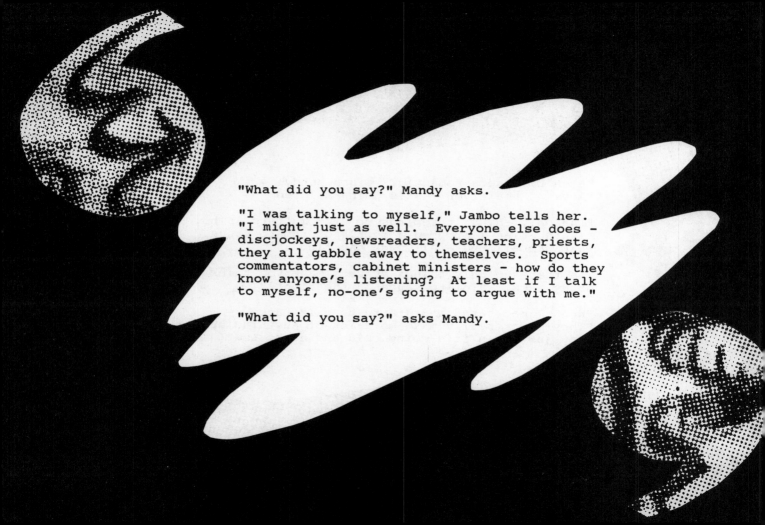

"What did you say?" Mandy asks.

"I was talking to myself," Jambo tells her.
"I might just as well. Everyone else does -
discjockeys, newsreaders, teachers, priests,
they all gabble away to themselves. Sports
commentators, cabinet ministers - how do they
know anyone's listening? At least if I talk
to myself, no-one's going to argue with me."

"What did you say?" asks Mandy.

Mandy finds Jambo in the cafe.
"Is that all you ever do? Sit in here
drinking tea?"

"I'm broke aren't I?" Jambo protests.
"I can't afford to do anything else."

Mandy pulls up a seat beside him,
"The price they charge for tea in here,
no wonder you're always broke."

Jambo keeps seeing invaders from outer space. He reckons he's the only one who can spot them. They disguise themselves like ordinary people, but Jambo can still pick them out - on trains and buses, or just walking down the street.

They give themselves away when they stand gazing in TV shop windows, or sneaking a look at the headlines on someone else's newspaper. Jambo can tell they're aliens by the way they shake their heads and say they can't understand the state this world's in. All these wars and pollution and football hooligans. Like it's got nothing to do with them.

So Jambo reckons they must come from outer space. Because if they were born on this planet and not some other one - and they don't like the state it's in - how come they haven't done something about it themselves by now?

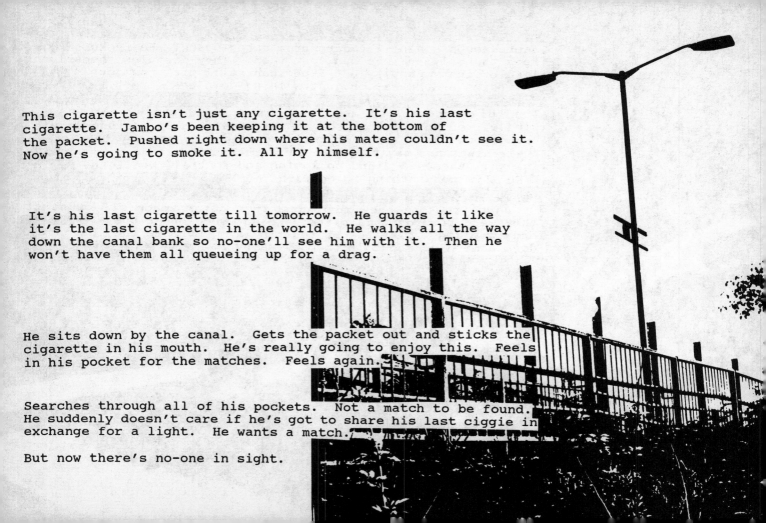

This cigarette isn't just any cigarette. It's his last
cigarette. Jambo's been keeping it at the bottom of
the packet. Pushed right down where his mates couldn't see it.
Now he's going to smoke it. All by himself.

It's his last cigarette till tomorrow. He guards it like
it's the last cigarette in the world. He walks all the way
down the canal bank so no-one'll see him with it. Then he
won't have them all queueing up for a drag.

He sits down by the canal. Gets the packet out and sticks the
cigarette in his mouth. He's really going to enjoy this. Feels
in his pocket for the matches. Feels again.

Searches through all of his pockets. Not a match to be found.
He suddenly doesn't care if he's got to share his last ciggie in
exchange for a light. He wants a match.

But now there's no-one in sight.

Jambo sits down and gets out his tobacco tin. Starts
to make himself a roll-up. He prefers to smoke
roll-ups these days. He likes to be able to sit there
and take his time. Likes to decide how much tobacco
to use. Then slowly roll a really fat one, or see if he
can get it as thin as a matchstick.

He likes the flavour better too. Likes to be able to
sit there and savour it. Yes, Jambo prefers roll-ups
these days.

He can't afford anything else.

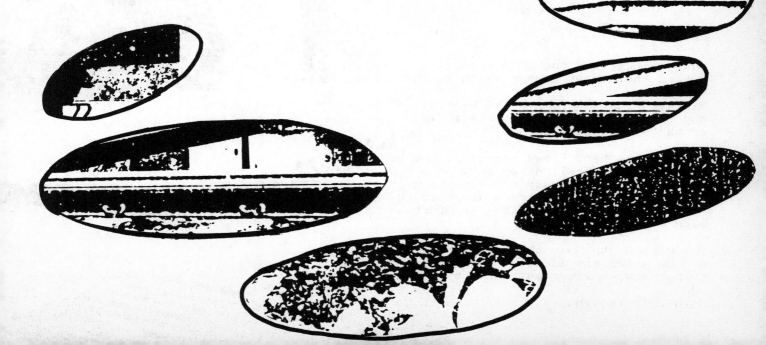

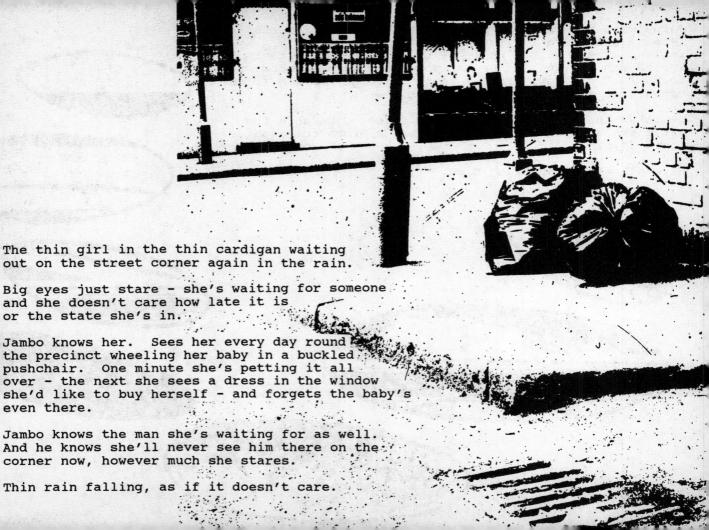

The thin girl in the thin cardigan waiting
out on the street corner again in the rain.

Big eyes just stare - she's waiting for someone
and she doesn't care how late it is
or the state she's in.

Jambo knows her. Sees her every day round
the precinct wheeling her baby in a buckled
pushchair. One minute she's petting it all
over - the next she sees a dress in the window
she'd like to buy herself - and forgets the baby's
even there.

Jambo knows the man she's waiting for as well.
And he knows she'll never see him there on the
corner now, however much she stares.

Thin rain falling, as if it doesn't care.

Jambo finds her sitting on the stairway. She's not crying or anything. She's just sitting there, staring. Jambo stops and stares back at her, but she doesn't move. Only her fingers, fidgeting, as if she's knitting, but there's nothing there.

Jambo tries to remember if she lives in this block. But she's not the sort of woman you'd notice if you saw her anywhere else, going round the shops.

Plump face under a scarf. A little bit of makeup that looks like it's still there from the night before. Dull coat pulled close around her. It's sunny outside, but it must be cold sitting here on the stairs. Tights with holes in and a pair of dirty plimsolls.

And her fingers are full of rings. He tries to see if one's a wedding ring, but her hands never stay still long enough.

Jambo stands and watches her. She must know he's there. He wishes she'd say something, even if it's only to tell him to go away. He wishes she'd cry, or scream, or anything. But she just sits there on the cold concrete staircase, staring at nothing that Jambo can see.

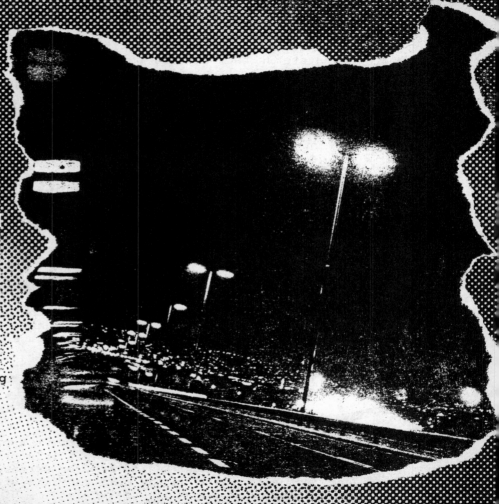

Jambo hangs round the
transport cafe,
watching the tankers
haul off the motorway.
Itches to climb inside
one and drive, high on
power and diesel fumes.

Then he'd stroll in here
in his oily overalls,
sit down with the crossword
and a mug of latenight
coffee and pretend to
ignore all the girls who
are sitting round ignoring
Jambo now.

Jambo sneers at his
reflection in the window,
trying to get that
expression on his face -
that look that says you're
bored senseless with driving
long distance trailers.

Jambo doesn't know how they
do it, without even the
flicker of a grin between
clenched teeth that lets on
how great it really is.

Jambo keeps looking at the girl in the slit skirt.
He knows she goes with Big Tony. He knows Big Tony's
not around. He wonders what to do.

He looks into her eyes for some kind of sign - like
let's meet outside about half past nine. The screen
goes blank. Jambo stops to think. He looks over again
just in time to see her wink.

So he walks over, cool and slow, planning to ask
if there's somewhere she'd like to go. She keeps
giving him this funny kind of grin, so he keeps right on
moving in. And when she winks again and keeps nodding
her head, he reckons all his thoughts shouldn't be left
unsaid.

So he starts to drool his opening line, and it seems
to him he's doing fine till his words dry up and she's
still just sitting there giving him this crazy stare,
so Jambo turns round and looks straight across the floor,
and there's Big Tony standing right there in the door.

Mandy stops. Shop window filled with wanting. She wants that dress she wants that shirt she wants that skirt she wants those shoes. She wants this she wants these she wants those.

Wants it all more than herself. She hates herself. She wants to live in that shop window and watch the street shift by looking at her. Not looking at her. Looking at her clothes.

Mandy likes getting
dressed up. She likes
putting on her best
blouse and her best
skirt and her best
shoes and her new tights.

Then she likes going to
the pictures with Jambo.
And sitting there in the
dark where no-one can see
her, so it wouldn't
really matter what
she was wearing.

And Jambo keeps complaining
he can't hear the film
because Mandy keeps
complaining how much her
best shoes hurt her feet.

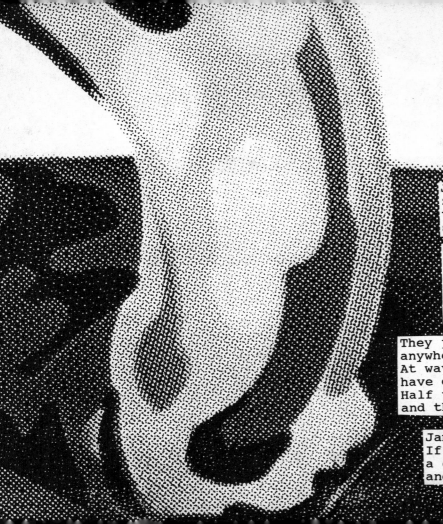

Jambo loves the way movie cameras
zoom in on the action. A bad skid,
the gun muzzle pumping. Blood
spurting out.

Something goes wrong in love scenes
though. Jambo used to hate
love scenes. He always reckoned
they were too slow.
But now he knows it's not that
at all. It's the lousy camerawork.

They just seem to point the camera
anywhere. At the ceiling. At the floor.
At waves crashing on the beach that
have got nothing to do with the story.
Half the time it's out of focus,
and they **never** zoom in on the action.

Jambo can't understand.
If you went to the pictures and saw
a car chase like that, you'd walk out
and ask for your money back.

Jambo's going to the movies. He queues up to wait
for a bus. When the bus comes the seats are all
full so he has to stand all the way.

Jambo's going to the movies. He waits in the queue
outside the picture house. Shuffling slowly round
the corner. He gets sick of reading the names of all
the rock bands on the back of the jacket of the lad
in front. Jambo doesn't like any of them anyway.

Jambo's going to the movies. He stands inside and waits
for his ticket and then queues up for his orange juice
and popcorn. And then he has to wait for the girl with
the torch to come and find him a place.

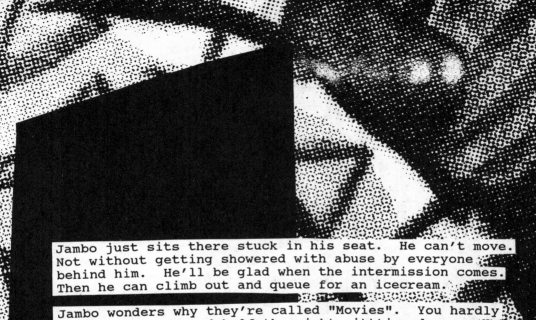

Jambo just sits there stuck in his seat. He can't move.
Not without getting showered with abuse by everyone
behind him. He'll be glad when the intermission comes.
Then he can climb out and queue for an icecream.

Jambo wonders why they're called "Movies". You hardly
move at all. Spend half the night sittting down or
standing still.

Jambo reckons he should make a real life movie about
queueing for buses, queuing in shops, standing
in dole queues. Waiting for Saturday night to come
just so you can queue up and go to the movies.

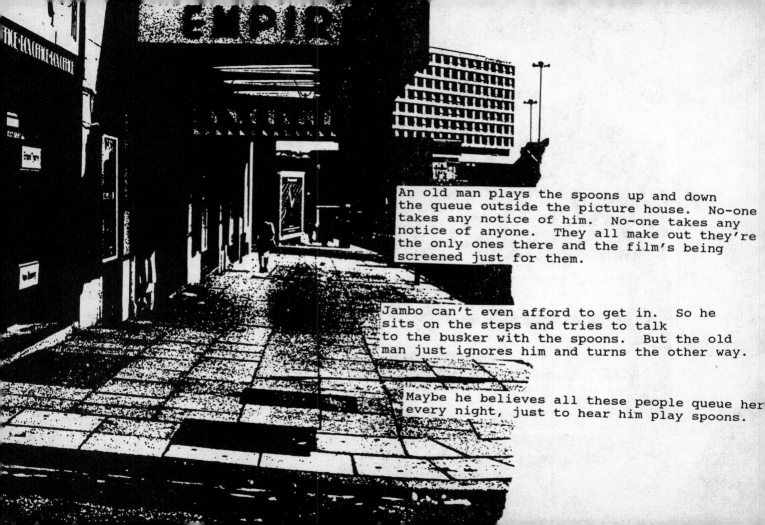

An old man plays the spoons up and down
the queue outside the picture house. No-one
takes any notice of him. No-one takes any
notice of anyone. They all make out they're
the only ones there and the film's being
screened just for them.

Jambo can't even afford to get in. So he
sits on the steps and tries to talk
to the busker with the spoons. But the old
man just ignores him and turns the other way.

Maybe he believes all these people queue her
every night, just to hear him play spoons.

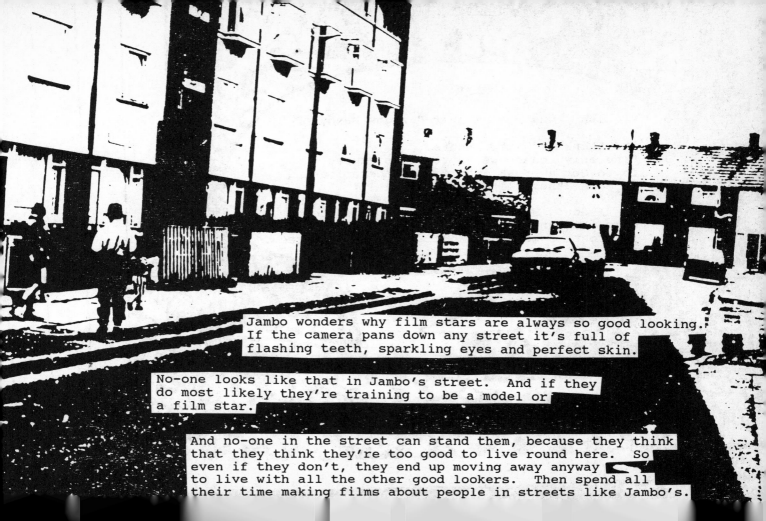

Jambo wonders why film stars are always so good looking.
If the camera pans down any street it's full of
flashing teeth, sparkling eyes and perfect skin.

No-one looks like that in Jambo's street. And if they
do most likely they're training to be a model or
a film star.

And no-one in the street can stand them, because they think
that they think they're too good to live round here. So
even if they don't, they end up moving away anyway
to live with all the other good lookers. Then spend all
their time making films about people in streets like Jambo's.

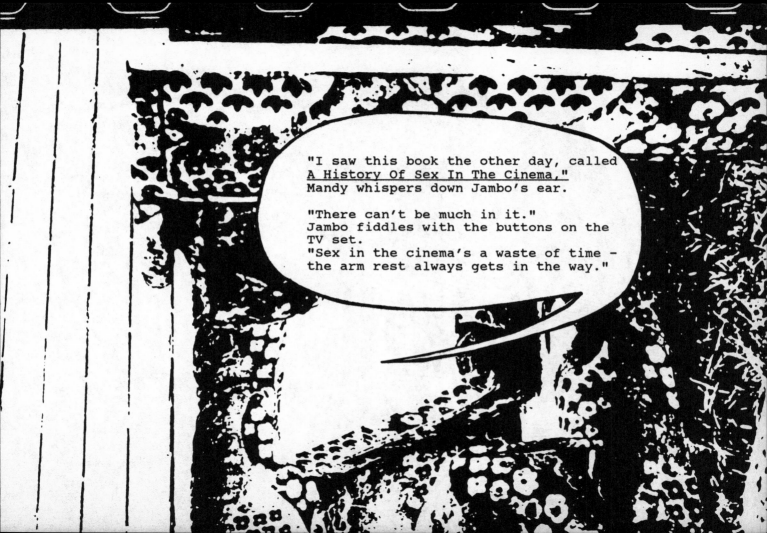

RUBBARITE L^{td}
SPONGE RUBBER
MANUFACTURERS

The man in the grey overcoat
who gets the train into town
at the same time every morning
has never met Jambo.

He never wants to meet Jambo.
He has these nightmares
about Jambo - as big as
the Incredible Hulk, as agile
as Spider Man.

He must be. How else could he
paint his name across the top
of every bridge and half way up
the brick embankment all along
the railway line?

What he'll never know is that
every night Jambo has a
nightmare too, where he gets
ordered from room to room
along a maze of silent corridors
by a mysterious man in a grey
overcoat who looks just like
the man on the train.

Jambo just sits. Silence in his head.
So loud he can't hear anything else.

He tries to move, but he can't. Silence
hanging on to him, heavy, dragging him
down.

Jambo is blinded by silence. There is
nothing else now. Nothing else in the room.
No room. No street outside the window.
Only Jambo sitting in the silence.

He decides the only thing to do
is make friends. Jambo starts to talk
to the silence.

The train pulls in to the station. Jambo looks for the name.
He doesn't want to miss his stop.

This station seems to be called "WAY OUT".

But everything looks the same as home. Rows of factories
and houses. Tower blocks stacked up to the sky. Jambo
wonders why he bothered coming.

But as soon as he gets out of the station and asks someone
the way, it's not the same at all. More like a foreign language.
Jambo's not too sure if he knows where he's going, even when
he's been told.

And he's not too sure about the way a gang of lads dressed
the same as him but with scarves a different colour
are watching him from across the road.

Jambo reckons what he'd really like to do is turn back round
and go home. But there's not even any signs saying "WAY OUT"
anymore - just strange streets and names he's never heard before
painted very tall on the walls.

Jambo stoned. Cigarettes explode. Thin fingers unpeel and broken. The petrol pumps are melting. A skeleton driving an ambulance and all the streetlamps laughing.

Jambo hangs onto the wall like a used crucifixion. His feet are tears. His eyes are bleeding. He can hear slow voices aching inside him, whispering his name over and over again.

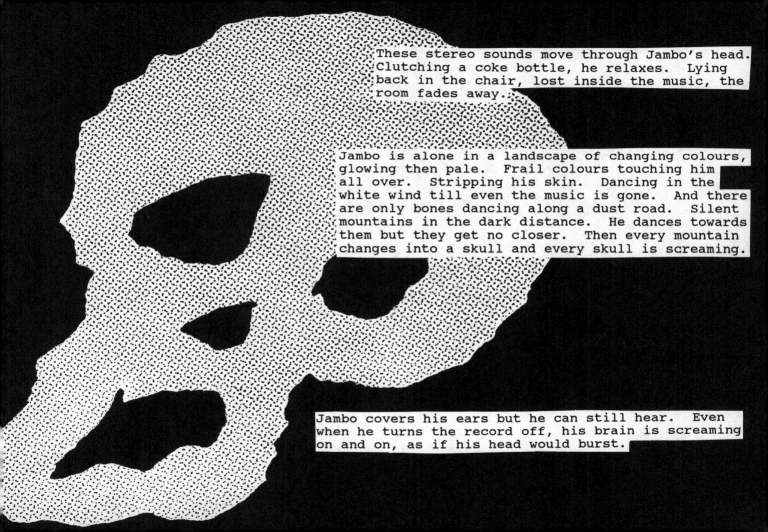

These stereo sounds move through Jambo's head.
Clutching a coke bottle, he relaxes. Lying
back in the chair, lost inside the music, the
room fades away.

Jambo is alone in a landscape of changing colours,
glowing then pale. Frail colours touching him
all over. Stripping his skin. Dancing in the
white wind till even the music is gone. And there
are only bones dancing along a dust road. Silent
mountains in the dark distance. He dances towards
them but they get no closer. Then every mountain
changes into a skull and every skull is screaming.

Jambo covers his ears but he can still hear. Even
when he turns the record off, his brain is screaming
on and on, as if his head would burst.

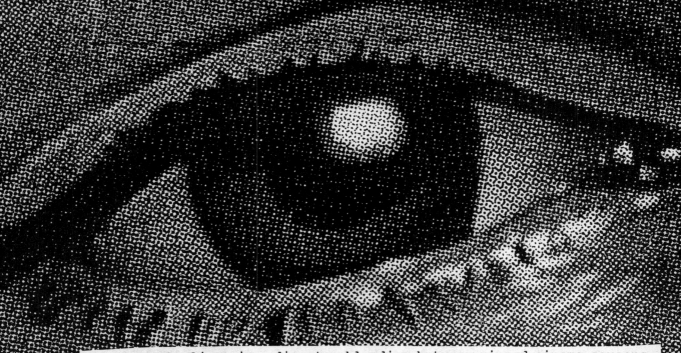

Jambo lives in a disaster bleeding between ripped cinema screens.
Cracked tower blocks. Music ugly as aching sirens. Streets
alive with walking suicides.

Jambo heaves the fruit machine hard against the wall in the
all-night coffee bar. The colours blur like burnt out nerves.
Click and whirr, spin and stop.

Every time every line's a loser, every time.

Jambo angry. Exploding like a broken TV tube. Scream of silence no-one ever sees breaking out and waking the street.

Heavy blood punching through his head. Suddenly everything's too fast like a crazy cartoon, only it isn't funny. Nobody laughs.

Sound of sirens like a dream, like a nightmare. Howling. Light flashing on and off, on and off. He can't stop. He wants to switch everything off but every channel's jammed open wide. And the howling echoing round and round, round and round, running blind trying to find some way to escape out from between the houses.

Jambo gets kidnapped.

He sits in the empty house holding himself hostage.
No-one can hear him when he shouts through the window.

He starts to write ransom notes on pages ripped
from a stolen cheque book. Stands at the open window and
floats them down into the street.

When his mates come to rescue him they find the house is
deserted. They wait around, shuffling, clutching the cans
of lager all the messages said to bring.

DANGEROUS
BUILDING

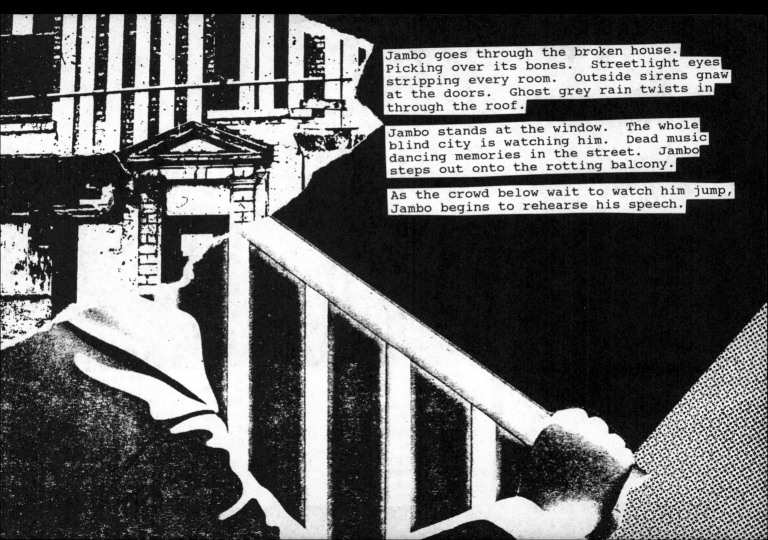

Jambo goes through the broken house. Picking over its bones. Streetlight eyes stripping every room. Outside sirens gnaw at the doors. Ghost grey rain twists in through the roof.

Jambo stands at the window. The whole blind city is watching him. Dead music dancing memories in the street. Jambo steps out onto the rotting balcony.

As the crowd below wait to watch him jump, Jambo begins to rehearse his speech.

This street is Jambo's
comic strip.

The bit between each
lampost is a different
frame.

Jambo skidding down
the pavement - "BAM" -
"SPLAT" - "KAPOW!"

Posing as he goes.

Jambo is a superman
saving the world.
Jambo is a Mafia
hitman. Jambo is a
football ace, a spy,
a film star. Jambo
can be whoever he
wants to be in his
own cartoon.

But how can he escape
from the final frame,
round the corner and
down the next street,
unless he's got a
punchline to leave on?

SEE NEXT WEEK'S
THRILLING EPISODE

"Dave Ward, in his long poem _Jambo_, has a character who embodies all the cultural content of the Toxteth riots."

Jeff Nuttall: THE LITERARY REVIEW

"_Jambo_ links together into a running commentary of his lifestyle."

THE FACE

"An excellent cartoon-like look at the absurdities of urban life."

RECORD MIRROR

"A reflection in words and graphics on what it's like to be unemployed."

SMASH HITS

"_Jambo_ is an excellent new book."

MELODY MAKER

"I like these poems very much - their power is cumulative."

BLAKE MORRISON

"It's _our_ Waste Land."

PETE FAULKNER

"I relate to your book in lots of ways - it really got through. I took it to the youth club and everyone enjoyed it. It made us really want to do something about unemployment."

WENDY ABBOTT: letter from a reader in Northampton.

"It's the best book I've read. _Jambo_ is like a good single that you want to play to your mates. I want to keep reading it to mine."

STEPHEN HILL: letter from a reader in Chichester.